ALEX BOYD FRSA is a photographer, curator and writer based in the west of Scotland. Until recently he lived in the Outer Hebrides. His work has been widely exhibited internationally with solo exhibitions at the Scottish Parliament, as well as group exhibitions at the Royal Academy, Royal Ulster Academy and Royal Scottish Academy. His work is held in the collections of the National Galleries of Scotland, The Royal Photographic Society, the Royal Scottish Academy, the V&A and the Yale Centre for British Art in the US. His first book *St Kilda: The Silent Islands* was shortlisted for the Saltire Society First Book Award in 2018. He is a contributing arts editor for *The Island Review* and *Art North*. He is currently undertaking a PhD on Scottish Photography.

By the same author

St Kilda: The Silent Islands, Luath, 2018
Isle of Rust: A Portrait of Lewis and Harris, Luath, 2019

Hirta

A Portrait of St Kilda

ALEX BOYD

Luath Press Limited

EDINBURGH

www.luath.co.uk

First published 2019

ISBN: 978-1-913025-05-2

The paper used in this book is recyclable. It is made
from low chlorine pulps produced in a low energy,
low emission manner from renewable forests.

Printed and bound by
iPrint Global Ltd., Ely.

Typeset in 10.5 point Sabon by Main Point Books, Edinburgh

Contents

To those who conserve our wild places.

Acknowledgements

Thank you to Dr Kevin Grant for his support and to Martin Martin for his writings. Thanks also to The National Trust for Scotland, Angus Campbell at Kilda Cruises, and the team at Luath, especially Maia Gentle, Lauren Grieve and Gavin Mac-Dougall. Heartfelt thanks to Jennie Renton and Coreen Grant at Main Point Books, who brought the book together. Thanks also to Andrew Aiton, Lachlan Young, David Henning, Louise Gallagher and Colin Miller. Many thanks also to my father David for his encouragement, and of course my wife Jessica who was my companion to the islands.

A Note on Martin Martin

Martin Martin (Màrtainn MacGilleMhàrtainn), a native of Skye, made a voyage to St Kilda in 1697 as part of a larger project to map the Western Isles headed by John Adair. His account of this journey was published in 1698 as *A Late Voyage to St Kilda*. Quotes from this volume are interspersed throughout this book.

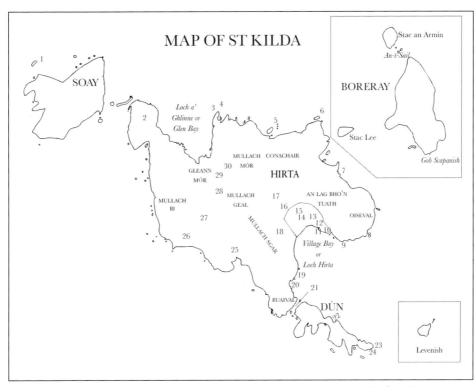

MAP OF ST KILDA

SOAY

1

Loch a' Ghlinne or Glen Bay

2
3 4
5
6

BORERAY

Stac an Armin
An-t-Sàil

Stac Lee

Gob Scapanish

MULLACH CONACHAIR
MÓR
GLEANN
MÓR
30
29
28

HIRTA

7

MULLACH
BI
MULLACH
GEAL
17
16
AN LAG BHO'N
TUATH
15
14 13
12
11 10

OISEVAL

27
18
8

26
25

MULLACH SGAR

Village Bay
or
Loch Hirta

9

19
20
21

RUAIVAL

DÙN

22

23
24

Levenish

1.	Am Plastair	11.	Church	21.	Caolas an Duin
2.	The Cambir	12.	Pier	22.	Geo na Ruideig
3.	Gob na h-Airde	13.	Factor's House	23.	Gob an Duin
4.	Geo na h-Airde	14.	Lady Grange House	24.	Gob na Muce
5.	Bradastac	15.	Graveyard	25.	Leathaid a' Sgithoil Chaoil
6.	Mina Stac	16.	Amhuinn Mór	26.	Lover's Stone
7.	The Gap	17.	Creagan Breac	27.	Claigeann an Tigh Faire
8.	Rudha an Uisige	18.	Gearraidh Ard	28.	Amhuinn a' Ghlinne Mhoir
9.	Point of Coll / Rudh Challa	19.	Uamh Cailleach Bheag Ruaival	29.	Airidh Mhór
10.	Manse	20.	Geo Chile Briannan	30.	Amazon's House

Introduction

Roger Cox, Arts Editor, *The Scotsman*

St Kilda – you don't exist. Your name is just a faint cry made by the birds that make their home on the high cliffs at the furthest edge of the United Kingdom, beyond the outermost of the Outer Hebrides.

SO BEGINS THE memorable entry on St Kilda in Judith Schalansky's *Atlas of Remote Islands*, subtitled 'Fifty Islands I Have Not Visited and Never Will'. First published in German in 2009, replete with beautiful retro-style maps, the atlas was translated into English the following year and has been described as 'gorgeous, lyrical and whimsical' by *Time* and 'utterly exquisite' by Robert Macfarlane. It even won Germany's award for the Most Beautiful Book of the Year.

Yet, for all the praise it has received, the book's entry on St Kilda is a little misleading. For a start, it describes the islands as 'uninhabited'. Technically, perhaps, there may not be any permanent residents but the Ministry of Defence (MOD) maintains a permanent presence there, as does the National Trust, which caters for the boatloads of tourists who land in Village Bay every summer. And then there's that rather breathless introduction. Granted, there is something undeniably romantic about the place – its splendid isolation, its intriguing history, its dramatic, perpendicular geography – but is there a danger that, by over-romanticising St Kilda, we fail to understand it properly? That seems to be the thesis of an admirably clear-sighted series of pictures by photographer Alex Boyd.

Boyd is based in the Outer Hebrides, which has enabled him to make multiple trips to St Kilda over several years and, while he can't claim to be a native St Kildan, he can at least see the place through the eyes of an islander. Boyd explained in his previous book *St Kilda – The Silent Islands* that he wanted to respond to the islands 'in a way which did not obscure the true St Kilda' and that, in order to do this, he decided to

document the military presence as well as the natural beauty of the islands and the ruins of Village Bay, to show a more balanced view, something which in truth is still rarely seen.

The portrait he paints of St Kilda then, in photographs produced using a medium format camera previously owned by the English landscape photographer Fay

Godwin, is very much 'warts and all', the warts being the decidedly unromantic buildings constructed on the island during the 20th century by the MOD. When he first visited St Kilda, what fascinated Boyd was 'something absent from the countless tourist images of the islands, and much less sympathetic to the surroundings; a Cold War military base'.

Therefore many of the pictures in that book, and in *Hirta – A Portrait of St Kilda* are of military infrastructure – of radar towers looming out of the mist on Mullach Mór, of the pebble-dashed radar installation at Mullach Sgar and of the brutalist 1970s power station in Village Bay.

There are also more familiar St Kilda scenes – of ruined blackhouses and of the towering sea cliffs of Stac Lee and Stac an Armin – but Boyd's intention is clearly to give us the complete picture of the island.

Boyd's photographs, as in his previous book, are informed by the writings of Dr Kevin Grant, an archaeology officer with Historic Environment Scotland who was previously St Kilda Archaeologist for the National Trust for Scotland.

Rather than seeing St Kilda as significant only because of what it can tell us about the past (as you might reasonably expect an archaeologist to do), Grant instead sees it as not all that different to the rest of the Hebridean archipelago and of just as much contemporary relevance. Historically, he suggests, the islands have been both connected to the nearby Outer Hebrides and also fairly typical of them. And today, he points out,

the islands' economy is almost exactly the same as the neighbouring Uists in that its two main pillars are tourism and the Ministry of Defence.

Grant, reflecting on his time on Hirta, wrote:

after three years living on the islands, I believe that the most precious part of St Kilda is its present-day community.

And, reflecting on Boyd's earlier book of St Kilda pictures, he added:

I hope that this collection of images... will encourage others to value the community of people who live and work there today at least as much as the long-lost one of 1930.

Reproduced by kind permission of Scotsman Publications Ltd.

Tourist boats in Village Bay

Angus Campbell, skipper of *Orca II*, is assisted by a crewman as he prepares a dinghy to ferry tourists to shore. Transit by small boats is the only way to land in St Kilda.

Boreray

It has been speculated that Boreray is the home of an Iron Age wheelhouse and a series of field systems. The remains of a small village on the island show that early settlers maintained an existence on this most inhospitable of locations.

Ruined cottages, Village Bay

The abandoned cottages of St Kilda are one of the most obvious reminders of the evacuation of the island in 1930. Many have been restored by National Trust work parties, returning them to their original condition – one such example houses a museum, while others serve as accommodation for National Trust volunteers.

Hiort: A Short History

Alex Boyd

The last and outmost Isle is named Hirta… on this Isle are a great number of sheep… The Isle is circled on every side with rocky crags, and no boats may land on it, but alone at one place…

Hector Boece, first principal of the
University of Aberdeen, 1527

RISING OUT OF the depths of the North Atlantic, the great cathedral-like sea stacks of Stac Lee and Stac an Armin and the jagged outlines of the islands of Hirta, Dùn, Levenish, Borerary and Soay make up one of the most famous groups of islands in the world, the archipelago of St Kilda.

It is a place that once seen is not soon forgotten, and a place of pilgrimage for thousands of tourists every year, although few make it out to the sheltered waters of Village Bay.

Owned and cared for by the National Trust for Scotland, St Kilda is a dual UNESCO World Heritage site, one of the few in the world awarded for both its important natural environment, and its status as a place of great cultural significance.

The names we have given to the islands reflect our own impressions of a place which in the minds of many lie far off in the west, 100 miles distant from mainland Scotland, surrounded by the treacherous waters of the North Atlantic.

From 'Britain's Loneliest Island' to the 'Islands at the Edge of the World', the archipelago is often considered to be an outlier both physically and culturally from the British Isles, a place where a separate, supposedly more basic existence took place in an environment whose stark natural beauty is matched by its harsh and unforgiving location. This is a place where the highest sea cliffs in the United Kingdom tower above the often fierce waters below; where winds have been so violent that the modern inhabitants of the islands have had to be evacuated as the speeds have reached 144 miles per hour – fierce gales sweep across Hirta for over 70 days a year.

The origins of the islands may also be reflected in their name. While we are uncertain of the exact name given to the earliest settlers of the islands, we do know that through a series of errors made by cartographers, the name does not derive from a fictitious saint, and instead may derive from the Norse *skildir*, meaning shield.

This name may refer to the shape of Hirta, whose form, like the rest of St Kilda was forged in the heart of a now extinct ring volcano, whose molten magma core lies several kilometres to the north-east in the seas between Hirta and Borerary.

The basalt and gabbro which make up the islands today were formed during the Tertiary period which, from a geological standpoint at 55 million years old, are far younger than the 3,000-million-year-old Lewisian gneiss which they broke through, one of a series of huge volcanoes which stretched down to the Isle of Arran.

Over the millennia the once colossal peaks and ridges of this now lost volcano have, through the actions of weathering, glaciers and the sea, been eroded down to what we see today, which is the remains of the magma cores once held deep beneath the earth, perhaps most visible in the cliffs of Hirta herself.

Perhaps the best way to visualise how St Kilda once was is to examine undersea maps of the islands, observing the way in which the entire volcanic complex extends far beyond them, a circular shield rising abruptly from the depths of the seabed below. It is here in the undersea environment that the islands hide some of their most stunning geology, away from the eyes of most visitors, unknown to the St Kildans, and today the refuge of sports divers who know of the dangers of the swell and the surge, but also of the wonders of what lies beneath.

A special area of conservation, the waters around St Kilda can be startlingly clear, some of the cleanest in the British Isles due to the lack of pollution. This results in a diverse undersea environment with colourful flora and fauna, from jewel anemones to kelp and soft corals lining the walls of impressive sea caves. Of these, the most interesting are 'the tunnel' which, at 40m in length, completely passes through Am Plastair, the sea stack at the foot of Connachair and the hidden sea arch below Sgarbh Stac which, at 20m high and 30m wide, provides a spectacular place for the seals of Boreray to explore.

The first people would not arrive on Hirta until long after the slow retreat of the last ice age. The island, the largest of the archipelago, with its isolated position and fertile glens, offered protection from invasion as well as access to the seas for fishing and trade.

While very little evidence of Neolithic settlement survives – much of it perhaps lost under the continually changing landscape of Village Bay – two sherds of Hebridean pottery from this time period were discovered in 1996. Perhaps journeys were made from nearby Uist, from which St Kilda can clearly be seen, and early attempts at settlement attempted during this period.

Items from the Bronze and Iron Ages are more numerous, with examples of tools such as scrapers, grinders and pounders, as well as unworked flint, all being found across Hirta.

Debate around specific locations for early settlements such as roundhouses, huts and field systems on Hirta have caused debates with modern archaeologists, with examples of funerary sites being confined to historical anecdotes from the resident minister Neil Mackenzie, who wrote of such places having been discovered in the 1830s during clearance work. From his descriptions, these are believed to possibly be Bronze Age cists, but we cannot be entirely sure.

The discovery of the souterrain, a type of underground structure, known as Taigh an t-Sithiche (the House of the Fairies) is one of the more obvious signs on Hirta of settlement during the Iron Age period. Uncovered and surveyed many times since its rediscovery in the 1840s, it has revealed interesting fragments and can be visited today in Village Bay. It appears that this structure existed alongside that of a farm, and that continued habitation of the island was established during this period, with the diets of islanders supplemented by fowling, something St Kildans would become synonymous with in later centuries.

The islands would eventually join the Kingdom of Norway after 900 AD with the Viking colonisation of much of Scotland, then known as the home of the Pictish Tribes. The Outer Hebrides remained the domain of Norse speakers, and it is from them that many of the names of this area take their origins. On Hirta, this is obvious in the names of the hills, such as Ruaival (Red Hill), Oiseval (East Hill) and of course the islands themselves, with Soay (Sheep Island) and Boreray (Fort Island). The first recorded entry for Hirta appears during this time with 'Hirter' being recorded in the journal of an Icelandic Bishop whose ship sheltered in the bay in 1202.

With the defeat of the Vikings at the Battle of Largs in 1263, ownership of the islands would once again change, with possession of the archipelago falling to King Alexander III of Scotland, who then passed it on to the Lords of the Isles, the much feared Viking/Gaelic rulers of the Hebrides, the descendants of the warlord Somerled. So it would be until they too would fall, and the islands passed to the MacDonald Clan of Skye in the late 15th century.

By the 16th century, a settlement was well established on the island of Hirta, with the Dean of Argyll and the Isles, Donald Munro, making a visit to the island now known in Gaelic as Hiort, and observing the healthy livestock and farming conditions of the island, while lamenting the lack of proper education and religious instruction in the village (Am Baile).

This would, of course, all change by the time of the visit of celebrated writer and traveller Martin Martin (Màrtainn MacGilleMhàrtainn) in 1697, whose *Description of the Western Islands of Scotland*, published in 1703, gave some of the earliest information about the lives of the islanders, recording that no less than three churches (Christ's Chapel, St Columba's and that of St Brianan) had been established on the outermost isle.

Martin recorded the everyday lives of the St Kildans, observing that shinty had become popular and that the islanders were fond of singing and dancing. A later visitor, the Reverend Kenneth Macaulay, remarked in his *History of St Kilda* (1764):

The power of music is felt everywhere: that divine art that charms enough to conquer the most savage heart. The St Kildans are enthusiastically fond of it, whether in the vocal or the instrumental way… the women while cutting down the barley in a field, or grinding their grain on their hand mills in the house, are almost constantly employed in this way; and the men, if pulling the oar, exert all their strength of their skill in animating the party, by chanting away some spirited songs, adapted to their business in hand.

Aside from noting that Hirta was home to 180 people, some 18 horses and 90 cattle, and that the villagers survived by also growing bere barley and oats, and hunting and consuming seabirds, Martin recorded various traditions observed by the inhabitants of the island, the most well-known of which is the story of the Mistress Stone:

In the face of the rock, south from the town, is the famous stone, known by the name of the mistress-stone; it resembles a door exactly; and is in the very front of this rock, which is twenty or thirty fathom perpendicular in height, the figure of it being discernible about the distance of a mile; upon the lintel of this door, every bachelor-wooer is by an ancient custom obliged in honour to give a specimen of his affection for the love of his mistress, and it is thus; he is to stand on his left foot, having the one half of his sole over the rock, and then he draws the right foot further out to the left, and in this posture bowing, he puts both his fists further out to the right foot; and then after he has performed this, he has acquired no small reputation, being always after it accounted worthy of the finest mistress in the world: they firmly believe that this achievement is always attended with the desired success.

Martin demurred on receiving an invitation from locals to experience this ceremony for himself, feeling that it might deprive him of both his life and his mistress. Whether or not these events were in fact an elaborate hoax played by the St Kildans or have a basis in reality, it is felt by many later chroniclers of Hebridean life such as Samuel Johnson that perhaps Martin may have been somewhat credulous.

Several decades after Martin's visit to Hirta, another visitor who has become closely associated with the story of the island made her first appearance in Village Bay. Rachel Chiesley, better known as Lady Grange, had been kidnapped on the orders of her husband, James Erskine, and was brought ashore in 1734, a prisoner who had unwillingly swapped the splendour of her Edinburgh home for a stone cleit, a supposed punishment for objecting to the philandering of her husband, and for threatening to uncover his treachery against the crown.

Trapped in a place from which there was no hope of escape, and where no one spoke English, she would spend her days largely drinking and sleeping. Letters relating to her imprisonment, in which she described Hirta as 'A viled neasty, stinking poor Isle', eventually made it back to Edinburgh, most notably to her lawyer. On St Valentine's Day in 1741, a sloop full of troops arrived at St Kilda to rescue Lady Grange, sadly too late. In the previous summer, she had already been moved to the Isle of Skye, where in 1745 she would see out her days in great discomfort.

The dark tale of Lady Grange is not the only one to be associated with the island. Martin Martin noted that 13 years prior to his visit, many islanders had died from an outbreak of leprosy, while in 1727 an outbreak of smallpox had a devastating effect on the population of Hirta. The situation had become so dire that in 1731 the island began to receive transports of people from the rest of the Hebrides to replace those lost to disease.

In 1812, the British politician and baronet Sir Thomas Dyke Acland would visit the islands, making one of the first sketches of island life in watercolour. He would return to the island again a decade later, leaving money to help build new houses. His schooner, *The Lady of St Kilda*, would later make the journey to Melbourne in Australia, and thus provided a name for another St Kilda in a much more temperate climate.

It was to Australia that 36 islanders, each seeking a better life, left Village Bay in 1852. Having spent their lives on the relative isolation of St Kilda, they had largely been kept out of reach of the many diseases and illnesses which had plagued other communities. Together with other Hebrideans they sailed south to a continent firmly in the grip of a Gold Rush. When their ship, *The Priscilla*, eventually arrived in Port Phillip, less than half their number had survived the voyage.

The arrival of Captain FWL Thomas on Hirta in 1860 on HMS *Porcupine*, and his subsequent three-day visit to the island as part of the Admiralty survey, have provided us with the earliest known photographs of the islands. Thomas was primarily interested in documenting the St Kildans themselves, creating a series of 16 portrait studies of the inhabitants of Village Bay, of women in doorways, and groups of men, boys and children – an anthropological study of those who called Hirta home.

Thomas also spent his time pursuing his research as an antiquarian and assisting in the mapping of

Village Bay itself. It is, however, his calotype images of the inhabitants which were the first to be circulated in small circles in mainland Scotland, and give us our first glimpse into the faces of island tradition-bearer Euphemia MacCrimmon, the island's midwife Betty Scott, the unnamed 'St Kildan Damsels Waiting for Husbands' and the catechist (religious instructor), Mr Kennedy. They show a barefooted community of simply dressed but pious Christians, many avoiding direct eye contact with the lens.

In 1877, regular steamer services to the island changed the dynamic of life on Hirta, bringing eager tourists such as the journalist WM Wilson of the *Ayr Observer* who wished to have 'A view of the natives, and of their social economy; an exhibition by the Cragsmen of their celebrated feats of fowling.' The arrival of Wilson and tourists like him, reveal that even by the late 1870s Hirta had – during the summer months at least – long adapted to the demands of visitors. It is well documented that by this stage St Kildans expected payment for photographs, for their fowling displays, and for the goods that they produced such as tweed and birds' eggs.

Stories and images of St Kilda started to become better known to a wider audience thanks to the photographs of Hirta, Boreray and the Stacs made by George Washington Wilson and Norman Macleod in the mid-1880s. Their views of island life, including the now famous image of the men gathering for the 'St Kildan Parliament', as well as the dramatic landscapes of the archipelago, enchanted audiences. They were shared as part of popular magic-lantern displays, as postcard images, and of course albumen prints. Artists and authors continued to visit the islands in great numbers, with George Seton's *St Kilda* of 1878 providing a variety of dazzling chromolithographs of Hirta, through to the celebrated publication in 1900 of Norman Heathcote's *St Kilda* which gave a more in-depth portrayal of the customs and lives of islanders, including some 80 illustrations made using a handheld camera, as well as watercolours.

It was the arrival of cheap, portable cameras in the late 19th century which have provided us with the largest record of images from the islands, as tourists flocked in their droves to visit the St Kilda archipelago. This, alongside the creation of a post-office on Hirta in the early 1900s, and the subsequent thousands of postcards sent from the islands (1,400 are recorded as being sent in 1907–8 alone) led to the islands being known to people far beyond the British Isles.

Village Bay's church was extended in 1906 to incorporate a new schoolhouse, a place where English was now taught alongside Gaelic. Life on the island seemed fairly stable, and the population reached almost 80. It was, however, the eventual outbreak of war on the European continent which would change life once again on Hirta. Its strategic position in the North Atlantic made it an ideal place to site a Royal

Navy signal station, allowing direct communication with the mainland for the first time in the islands' history.

Aside from the arrival and departure of trawlers, life continued as normal until the morning of 15 May 1918 when the war finally came to St Kilda. The German submarine U-90, under the command of Walter Remy arrived in Village Bay, and from what seems like a more gentlemanly period of warfare, sent a warning to the inhabitants that it was about to open fire. The crew trained its deck gun towards the wireless station and proceeded to fire 72 rounds into the intended target, destroying the station, damaging a storehouse, and inflicting damage on the manse and the church. No civilians were killed in the action, and the only loss of life being a lamb. Satisfied that her task had been accomplished, the U-boat slid out of the bay and back into the killing grounds of the North Atlantic, her next victim the troopship USS *President Lincoln*, one of 30 ships sunk during seven wartime patrols.

A response to this outrage appeared in the form of a four-inch naval gun which was installed on Hirta just before the end of the war. However, it was never fired in anger. It remains in position today, facing out toward Dùn.

The end of hostilities may have brought a sense of relief to the St Kildans. However, it had left a mark on the very nature of island life. With instant communication to the mainland and the wider world, a new money-based economy, and the enticement of less hostile environments in which to live, a gradual and noticeable erosion of the island's population began to occur. Numbers, especially those of young men, began to fall. The post-war settlement of 73 dropped to just 37 in 1928 – four men died from influenza in 1926. Several crop failures that decade, followed by the death in January 1930 of Mary Gillies, one of the island's young women, brought the situation facing the remaining islanders into sharp relief. Life on St Kilda could no longer continue as it had for centuries.

Together the islanders made the decision to evacuate to the mainland and, in August, two ships arrived in the bay. On the 27th, the remaining livestock were transferred aboard the *Dunara Castle* and the dogs who had served the islanders faithfully were taken out into the bay to be drowned, their fate deemed to be kinder than that of starvation.

Friday 29 August is, however, the date that will long be associated with the history of Hirta, the day that islanders said goodbye to their homes forever. Before locking their doors for the last time, each left an open Bible and a handful of oats on the table. At just after 7.00am HMS *Harebell* set a course for Morvern in Argyll with the islanders on board – 13 men, 10 women and 13 children. Many tears were shed as the familiar silhouette of the archipelago disappeared from view.

Those who left would in many cases go on to lead

eventful lives, several returning back to the islands on visits, some bringing their children to show them the places which had shaped them. The last of the original St Kildans, Rachel Johnson, passed away in 2016, having been one of the youngest evacuees at just eight years of age.

Following the loss of its community, Hirta was seldom visited, aside from passing fishing vessels and naval squadrons which patrolled the area. Slowly the abandoned homes began to fall apart, the harsh environment and winds undoing the work of generations of islanders.

The Second World War did not see a reoccupation of the islands and, instead, the Battle of the Atlantic which raged around the archipelago would add another tragic addition to the story of St Kilda. Situated directly in the flightpath of military operations, the islands provided the graves for several British Aircraft and their crews, which would unfortunately crash into the mist-shrouded hills and cliffs of Hirta and Soay. The remains of one of these aircraft, a Sunderland Flying Boat, can still be seen in situ in Gleann Mòr today.

It was during this period that one of the most bizarre stories around St Kilda emerged, as a claim was made on the island by Icelander Karl Kerulf Einarsson, also known as 'Cormorant XII Emperor of Atlantis', who styled himself the Duke of Saint Kilda. An eccentric artist, poet and writer, he remains something of a celebrated figure in his native Iceland, where he is also known as 'Dunganon'. He died in 1971, leaving behind several hundred works of art.

In reality, the islands were now under the ownership of the Marquis of Bute, who had been sold the islands by Sir Reginald MacLeod of MacLeod in 1931. Post-war, St Kilda found itself on the frontline of a new global conflict, that of the Cold War. In 1955, the Ministry of Defence decided to incorporate Hirta into a military testing area, a missile firing range which would stretch out to the west from Benbecula in the Uists.

In 1957, a new chapter in the islands' life would begin as, after 27 years of abandonment, a new community would be established by the military. Construction of a new concrete base on the island as part of 'Operation Hardrock' would see the addition of a barracks, radar installations, a canteen, a diesel power generator and even a sports hall. And 1957 also marks another significant event in the life of St Kilda, as ownership of the island was gifted to the National Trust for Scotland (NTS) from the Marquis of Bute. Today, the NTS and the Ministry of Defence work together to support work on the island, providing access through Army landing craft which land supplies, as well as the regular and familiar arrival of helicopters which land at 'St Kilda International Airport'.

Today, the island continues to attract thousands of visitors a year, each keen to witness this stunning dual UNESCO World Heritage site, a place where a long and at times tragic history sits alongside the realities of a modern military installation. It is a place which still continues to draw artists such as the printmaker Norman Ackroyd, the sculptor Steve Dilworth, the photographer Thomas Joshua Cooper, the composer Sir James MacMillan, and writers such as Will Self and Kathleen Jamie who have all made work relating to or inspired by the islands.

At the time of writing, the island is changing once more. The harsh angles and lines of the military base are, through the work of architects sympathetic to the beauty of Hirta, being softened, the buildings made more sustainable and, perhaps most importantly to the economy and long term story of the islands, more palatable to the eyes of those who step off the many cruise ships, tour boats and yachts which fill Village Bay in the summer months.

The work of the National Trust for Scotland has helped to repair and conserve the settlement of Village Bay, surveyed the thousands of structures located on the hills across the islands, and even produced a 3D scan of the archipelago. Along with the St Kilda Club, they continue to add new insights into the story of these fascinating islands.

A VISUAL JOURNEY
AROUND ST KILDA

The Inhabitants of St Kilda are almost the only People in the World who feel the Sweetness of true Liberty; what the Condition of the People in the Golden Age is feigned to be, that theirs really is.

The Workshop, No. 5 The Street

In the late 1950s, National Trust for Scotland work parties began to arrive on the island, tidying up collapsed walls, making repairs to the street and carrying out other basic forms of conservation work. There are 16 cottages in Village Bay, which form a gentle arc known as The Street. The majority remain in a state of ruin.

Restored cottages and museum, Village Bay

The cottages of Village Bay, abandoned during the evcuation of 1930, were left to decay until the military began restoring them in the 1960s. This began with house No. 1 in 1964, and was part of a wider effort to provide more permanent lodgings for the military staff stationed on Hirta.

Village Bay from Clash na Bearnich

A selection of tour boats and pleasure craft moored in Village Bay. During the summer months there are many visitors to the island, weather permitting. Among these are cruise liners, and it is not uncommon to find Hirta thronged with tourists. This explains the presence of a National Trust gift shop, located near the harbour.

Had he indeed travelled the universe he could scarcely have found a more solitary place for a monastic life.

Abhainn Ilishgil, Village Bay

The river which runs through Village Bay passes directly under the head dyke, and is one of several rivers to be found on the island. Its name translates as 'deep stream of the spring'. Others include Abhainn Gleshgill, which translates as 'shining stream in the gully'.

The Street

The former homes of The Street now lie abandoned, their previous owners now long departed. What little they left behind was finally removed by National Trust work parties in the 1950s, including beds and what remained of the roofs.

View across Village Bay

Oiseval dominates the scene to the east, while multiple eras of settlement can be seen in Village Bay, from the cleits and walled enclosures of an earlier era of settlement, to the 19th century blackhouses, and the much later Cold War era green buildings of the Ministry of Defence.

Blackhouse and byre

These ruins of the 19th century blackhouses sit side by side with earlier structures on The Street. These earlier structures still functioned as useful byres right up until the evacuation of 1930.

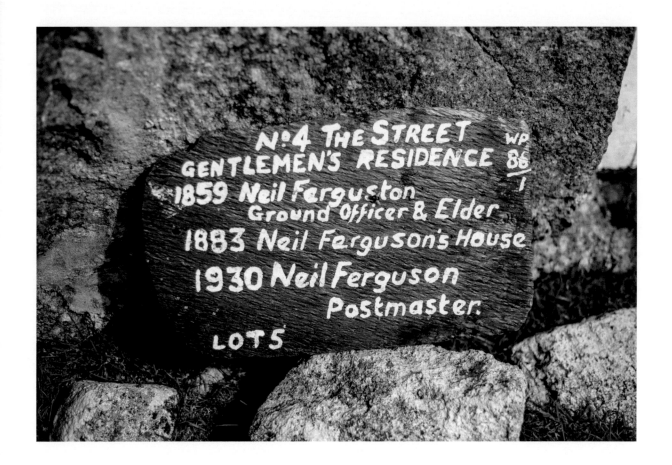

The Ferguson house, No. 4 The Street
Neil Ferguson's role as postmaster of Village Bay was a focal point of life on the island, for both locals and tourists. The tin-roofed post office that he once ran has long since been cleared.

The houses are of a low form, and the doors all to the North-East, to secure them from the shocks of the tempestuous South-West winds.

Conachair from Village Bay

Blackhouses are a traditional form of house built with drystone walls. Some 30 remain on Hirta,
the result of a visit in 1812 by Sir Thomas Dyke Acland, who found the earlier settlement to be
primitive and donated money for their construction to improve the lives of the islanders.

Cleitan, Village Bay

Aside from the ruins of homes in Village Bay, it is the cleitan which have come to be some of the best known structures on the islands. There are 1,200 of them throughout the archipelago, once used for the storage of peats, grain and food. It is thought that the cleitan are prehistoric in origin, and were in continual usage until the 1930s.

Village Bay from the slopes of Ruabhal
The landscape of Hirta has a long history of habitation, from the Bronze Age, to the evacuation
in 1930, to the eventual establishment of the new military base in the 1950s.

Village Bay, The Street

The long Street of Village Bay contains the ruins of the more modern blackhouses, built in the 1860s to replace earlier structures. After a severe storm it was found that they were not suited to the environment and many fell into disuse, becoming byres long before the evacuation.

The Street and Village Bay from above
The curve of The Street and the variety of structures which surround it can be seen here: to the rear cleitan and in the foreground, the circular wall of the cemetery.

This little village is seated in a valley surrounded with four mountains, serving as ramparts of defence, and are of many amphitheatres.

The factor's house, Village Bay
The factor's house was constructed in the 1860s for Norman MacRaild, factor to Sir John
Macpherson MacLeod. The building, of a simple design, accommodate some visitors to the island,
is today is the home of the island's warden and visiting researchers.

Soay sheep, Village Bay

The sheep of St Kilda are believed to be some of the earliest survivors of a neolithic breed, first brought to the island of Soay in the Neolithic period. These feral sheep which now roam free throughout Village Bay were established there after the evacuation in 1930, and are the subject of intense study by international scientists.

The manse

The Stevenson manse and the church are the only surviving examples left today, and as such are a scheduled monument. Following extensive reconstruction, the manse contains the offices of the National Trust for Scotland as well as a tourist shop run and maintained by the St Kilda Club.

Soay sheep

A familiar sight across the island, Soay sheep can be seen wandering everywhere. Living a relaxed life, one known as Old Green lived to the age of 23, producing an incredible 40 offspring. The majority in Village Bay have been tagged by scientists.

The ablutions block
Sitting across from the manse, the ablutions block was built in 1957 as part of the first military base, and used by officers. Today it is used by work parties and campers who visit the island.

The sheep in the Isle Soay are never milked, which disposes them to be the more prolific: there are none to catch them but the inhabitants, whom I have seen pursue the sheep nimbly down the steep descent, with as great freedom as if it had been a plain field.

Resting sheep, ablutions block
One particular detail noticed by visitors to Hirta is not just the abundance of Soay sheep, but also their relative size. They are diminutive compared to modern breeds, weighing less than a third of a domestic sheep.

Cemetery wall, Village Bay
The cemetery on Hirta, with its circular enclosure, is one of the most recognisable structures in Village Bay, and stands on the site of much older structures, including that of a medieval chapel which had fallen into disrepair by the mid-18th century.

The head dyke, Village Bay

The head dyke, built in 1834, encloses most of the structures of Village Bay, echoing the natural ampitheatre of the location created by four of Hirta's highest peaks: Oiseval, Conachair, Mullach Mór and Mullach Sgar.

Weather station, Ruabhal
This telemetry station on the slopes of Ruabhal provides important data on windspeed and direction, informing the mainland as to whether or not safe landings can be made on the island.

Power station, Village Bay

Constructed in 1970, the two storey power station houses four Mirlees Blackstone generators which provide power for the accommodation and radar sites across the island. The largest building in Village Bay, it is a structure which dominates the landscape, and for obvious reasons is generally excluded from images of the island. The low hum of the power station is sometimes the only sound heard in Village Bay at night.

The sea rises and rages extremely upon this rock: we had some curiosity, being invited by a fair day, to visit it for pleasure, but we found it very hazardous; the waves from under our boat rebounding from off the rock, and mounting our heads, we dared not venture to land.

Stone walls, cleits and Dùn beyond, Village Bay

The island of Dùn guards Village Bay against some of the worst excesses of the North Atlantic. In this image the crescent shape of Village Bay can clearly be discerned, with the military structures and ruins of the settlement further down the hill.

St Kilda International Airport
While perhaps not as luxurious as other airports, the simple waiting room located beside the helipad provides shelter from the worst of the elements.

Bulldozer

There are a number of military vehicles stationed on Hirta, including this D-6 Caterpillar Bulldozer, painted in a standard army green. The vehicle is primarily used to clear the landing ramp after winter storms, ensuring continuous access for army landing craft.

The feather store, Village Bay
The feather store has been used for a variety of purposes, from a place to hold church services to a storehouse for goods produced on the island. During WWI it was shelled and damaged by a U-boat which had come to destroy a Royal Naval signal station.

Feather store, window

The feather store, built some time prior to the 1820s, was restored by the National Trust for Scotland in 1986 and transformed from a completely ruinous state into the familiar building we see today.

This place may be reckoned among the strongest forts, natural or artificial, in the world; nature has provided the place with store of ammunition for adding on the defensive; that is, a heap of loose stones on the top of the hill.

Gun emplacement

Following an attack by a U-boat, it was felt that Hirta should be better protected during the First World War, and to this end this 4-inch naval gun was fitted in the dying days of that conflict. It has never been fired in anger, and today points harmlessly at visiting cruise ships.

Military buildings
The Ministry of Defence near Village Bay buildings are being modernised and have been painted green in an attempts to lessen their visual impact.

Ship's bell of the HMAV *Aghelia*, Village Bay
The bell of the *Aghelia*, a landing craft of the British Army which used to supply the military base in the 1960s. Designed to carry 350 tonnes of supplies, the role of these ships has largely been replaced by helicopters. The journey to and from supply bases on the Scottish mainland onboard these vessels was noted for not only being slow, but also arduous for crews and passengers.

Church aisle

Almost entirely devoid of decoration, the church is an austere place, as is typical of churches across the Outer Hebrides. The pulpit dates from the 1920s. To the right can be seen the door to the school classroom.

Collection box

A later addition to the island, this beautifully crafted elm donations box is marked on each side by the names of the islands in the archipelago.

They place the faces of their dead towards the East when they bury them, bewail their relations excessively, and upon these occasions make doleful songs, which they call laments.

The church

Designed by Robert Stevenson for the Free Kirk in 1826, the church today is interdenominational.
Simply rendered and appointed, it fell into disrepair after the evacuation and took several
decades to restore. The original bell was salvaged from the wreck of the SS *Janet Cowan* in 1864.

The classroom

The classroom on Hirta was built as an extension to the church in 1898. Funded by the Highland Committee of the Free Church of Scotland, it served its purpose for 32 years. It was finally repaired in 1980 by the military and given to the National Trust for Scotland in 2009.

Globe, the classroom (left): A faded and well-used globe found in the classroom on St Kilda.
Church window (right): The view from the church window, which is devoid of any decoration, looks directly at St Kilda's military defences, perhaps not the most fitting of subjects to contemplate.

Low tide, Village Bay

Looking west from near the feather store, this view of the beach at low tide shows where the army landing craft come ashore. While shallow here, the bay quickly and dramatically falls off into deep water and at times dangerous waves make landing impossible.

North-west from Ruabhal
This view along the spine of Ruabhal gives a good impression of the layout of Hirta. With Village Bay to the right and the long arm of the Cambir to the left, the peaks of Mullach Bi to the west and Conachair to the east can clearly be seen. In the middle are the installations of the MOD.

Every Bachelor-wooer is by an ancient custom obliged in honour to give a specimen of his affection for the love of his mistress.

Dùn from Ruabhal
The island of Dùn is separated from the rest of Hirta by Caolas an Dùin (the Straits of Dùn),
a narrow channel which was once bridged by a sea arch. A legend holds that the arch was
destroyed in a collision by a galleon of the Spanish Armada; more likely it collapsed during a storm.

The view to Dùn

On the other side of Village Bay is the island of Dùn (fort), which provides protection to the bay from the prevailing southwesterly wind. It is separated from Hirta by a narrow strait. The fort itself which gave the island its name is now long lost, but is believed to have been on Gob an Dùin, its seaward end.

The Mistress Stone

First published in 1698, Martin Martin's account of a journey to St Kilda mentions the Mistress Stone as a place where custom required the suitor to stand one-legged and peer over the edge to the abyss below, marking him out as worthy of any woman. Whether this custom was invented by the locals to amusingly mislead Martin or whether it has its roots in reality has yet to be ascertained.

Clais na Bearnach, Ruabhal

Near here stood St Brianan's, a thatched chapel mentioned by Martin Martin. Nothing remains of this early structure. Close by is Uamh Cailleach (Cave of the Old Woman) which takes its name from the legend of Fearchar and Dugan. These two men visited the island, terrorised the inhabitants, and an old woman hid within this cave to escape them, later emerging to identify the criminals.

Radar installation, Mullach Mór

The radar installations of Hirta were constructed primarily with the aim of tracking launches from the missile bases in South Uist. The facilities are equipped to monitor these launches, with the seas between Uist and St Kilda being used to test the first guided nuclear weapon, the Corporal Missile, in the early 1960s.

About two leagues and a half to the North of St Kilda is the rock Stack Lee, two hundred paces in circumference, and of a great height, being a perfect triangle turning to a point at the top; it is visible above twenty leagues distant in a fair day, and appears blue.

Radar installation, Mullach Mór

A number of radar facilities occupy the hilltops. The radar installation in the north, on the summit of Mullach Mór, tracks the rockets of the Deep Sea Range, an RAF missile range situated on South Uist.

Gleann Mhór

Gleann Mhór is believed to have been settled since the Iron Age, with the remains of habitation scattered across the valley floor. On the north side of Hirta, the glen forms a natural ampitheatre which mirrors that of Village Bay, and has long been used as a place of pasture.

Gleann Mhór shielings

This lesser known part of Hirta played an important role in the lives of St Kildans, providing islanders with access to valuable grazing land. At one time, this glen was filled with up to 40 cattle and numerous sheep, each helping to feed the islanders.

Gleann Mhór looking up to the radar installation on Mullach Mhór
The slopes of Mullach Mhór rise steeply from the valley floor of Gleann Mhór to a height of 361m.

Wreck of crashed aircraft,
Gleann Mhór
The wrecks of several Second World
War aircraft are to be found on
St Kilda, including a Beaufighter,
a Sunderland and a Wellington
bomber, all lost in accidents between
1943 and 1944.

The inhabitants here are originally descended of those of the adjacent isles, Lewis, Harris, South and North Uist, and Skye: both sexes are naturally grave, and of a fair complexion.

Entrance to the natural spring, Gleann Mhór

Towards the seaward end of Gleann Mhór lies the freshwater spring of Tobar Nam Buaidh (Well of the Virtues or of the Excellent Qualities). Wells such as these were often associated with the ability to cure those with ailments, with this example being said to cure deafness and nervous diseases.

Conachair and Geo na h-Airde sea cave from Gob na h-Aird

The sea cave of Geo na h-Airde is one of the largest on Hirta, and passes completely under the headland. Home to seals whose barking echoes throughout the cave, it can be accessed by climbing down its western side, providing one of the more memorable experiences on the island.

Gleann Mhór

Less well known than Village Bay, Gleann Mhór is Hirta's other main valley, a natural amphitheatre sweeping down to the sea. It contains many Iron Age remains, and is dotted with shielings as well as aircraft wreckage from the Second World War.

Gleann Mhór, with Soay behind

The island of Soay (Soaigh in Gaelic) takes its name from the Norse, translating as 'Island of the sheep', a fitting title as it is home to one of the oldest known breeds of sheep. A steep mountain peak rising from the seabed below, Soay is separated from Hirta by a narrow 500m channel.

Radar installations on Mullach Mór

The Decca radar stations on Hirta have the capability to photograph launches, and are now
managed by a civilian company, QinetiQ, who continue to monitor launches from the mainland.
The large telemetry mast was installed in the 1980s, and is visible from much of Hirta.

It deserves our consideration to reflect seriously upon the natural propensity and sagacity of these animals in their kind; which, if compared with many rational creatures, do far outstrip them, and justly obey the prescript of their natures, by living up unto that instinct that providence has given them.

The great skua

Also known as the Bonxie, and with a wingspan of up to 1.4m, these birds can often be seen sweeping low and aggressively at those who stray to close to their nests. Visitors are warned to carry sticks with them around Hirta, as the birds tend to attack at their highest point. Known for being completely unafraid of humans, they will attack smaller birds, and steal their food from others.

The Lover's Stone
The Lover's Stone, with its precarious drop over a precipice to the crashing waves of the Atlantic below, is a place associated with many myths and legends. It shares many of these stories with that of the Mistress Stone, located nearby on Ruabhal.

Puffins

Puffins can be found across the North Atlantic. On Dùn, where they were largely safe from predators, numbers have been in decline in recent years due to increased predation and problems with food supply. It is thought a quarter of all the UK's puffin population live on the St Kilda islands.

The cliffs of Conachair
At 430m in height, the cliffs of Conachair are the highest in the United Kingdom. In 1943 an RAF Beaufighter aircraft crashed approximately 100m from the summit, killing all onboard. The wreckage of the aircraft can still be seen today.

Mist on the road to Mullach Mór
The weather on St Kilda is notoriously changeable, with thick mist often descending quickly on the hilltops around Village Bay and obscuring everything in moments. The road is lined on both sides with cleitan.

The air here is sharp and wholesome; the hills are often covered with ambient white mists, which in winter are forerunners of snow, if they continue on the tops of the hills.

Military road to Mullach Mór

The military roads leading from Village Bay to the radar tracking stations on Mullach Mór were originally planned to be built from the abandoned ruins of Village Bay. Thankfully this plan was opposed by the National Trust for Scotland, and when the roads were eventually built in 1957, the material was taken from a new quarry built above the village at Creagan Breac.

Detail of enclosure, An Lag Bho'n Tuath

The enclosures of An Lag Bho'n Tuath are nestled in the hollow leading up to The Gap, a wide pass between Oiseval and Conachair. The ground here was suitable for summer grazing as well as growing food for the long winters on Hirta.

Cleitan along The Gap between Conachair and Oiseval
This route up to The Gap has long been a favourite for those visiting the island, as the view to
Boreray is one of the finest on Hirta.

The enclosures on the floor of An Lag Bho'n Tuath
The valley of An Lag Bho'n Tuath and the slopes of Conachair provided the population of Hirta with rich supplies of peat and turf for their fires.

Cliffs of Oiseval

The steep cliffs of Oiseval drop some 300m to the Atlantic below. Sheep still graze on some of the ledges, on which the remains of cleitan can be seen, often perilously close to the precipice. It is from these cliffs that St Kildan cragsmen descended to catch seabirds.

Their frequent discourses of climbing, together with the fatal end of several... is the fame to them, as that of fighting and killing is with soldiers.

Claigeann an Tigh Faire

According to an account written in 1928 by a J Mathieson, this series of cleits around the 'Skull' of Claigeann an Tigh Faire (Skull of the Watchhouse) were once manned day and night. They stand on the steep ridge leading up to the peak of Mullach Bi, and have a commanding view of the valley floor below.

Mullach Bi from Ruabhal

The precipitous cliffs of Mullach Bi, which reach a height of 358m, provided a place for St Kildans to collect birds and their eggs. On its grassy slopes is the location of at least one bothy, which is reached via a difficult descent from the cliff edge above.

Lone puffin, Mullach Bi

St Kilda is known for its huge puffin colonies, which have reached some 270,000 birds. Known for burrowing, they do not build nests and instead dig into cliff faces. During the summer months, care is taken to put out lights or draw curtains in order to stop pufflings being attracted to buildings.

Fulmars

Related to the albatross, fulmars can be seen around the cliff-faces of Hirta, riding on updrafts and keeping a close eye on visitors. Those who stray too close to their nests are rewarded with a foul-smelling oil, a defence which did not deter the St Kildans hunting them in large numbers. Aptly enough, the name fulmar is Norse in origin, fúll meaning foul, and már meaning gull.

Boreray and the Stacs

Perhaps one of the most familiar views associated with St Kilda, this vista can be seen from The Gap on Hirta. Boreray is the smallest of the Scottish islands to have a peak of over 1,000ft, making it a highly desirable choice for hill climbers, though very few manage to land there.

It is naturally fenced with one continued face of a rock of great height, except a part of the bay, which lies to the South-East, and is well defended generally with a raging sea.

Hirta with Soay behind

Leaving Hirta behind, the cliffs of Oiseval and Conachair can be seen to tower above the North Atlantic. No less impressive is Soay, an island which is rarely visited due to the difficulty in landing.

The cliffs of Boreray

Given the near verticality of its cliffs, it is incredible to realise that the island of Boreray has its own 'cleit village' – Cleitean MacPhàidein – three small bothies formerly used to shelter bird hunters.

Stac an Armin

This sea stack holds the rare distinction of being the last home in Great Britain of the great auk, a now extinct species of bird resembling a penguin. In 1840, a story was related to Henry Evans, a visitor to the island, who was informed that three days after capturing the bird the St Kildans killed, suspecting it of being a witch.

Gannet colony, Boreray

The sheer numbers of gannets living in close proximity to one another can clearly be seen in this image. The birds nest on any surface on the island which is not perpendicular, an impressive achievement given Boreray's steep topography.

Stac Lee (Stac Lì)

From the south Stac Lee appears to be broad, however from the west a hook-like profile is seen.
Rising from the depths like a needle, like much of the archipelago the remains of an extinct
volcano.

We put in under the hollow of an extraordinary high rock, to the North of this isle, which was all covered with a prodigious number of gannets hatching in their nests; the heavens were darkened by their flying over our heads.

Stac an Armin

From 15 August 1727 to 13 May 1728, three men and eight boys from Hirta were marooned on Stac an Armin. They returned to Hirta to discover that the smallpox outbreak which had broken out in their absence had wiped out most of the adult population.

Stac an Armin and Boreray

Stac an Armin has a long history of being climbed. While previously this was done solely to harvest eggs, since the late 1960s, climbers such as John Morton Boyd and Dick Balharry have made ascents to the peak. Today this is rare due to the extreme difficulty of landing on the island.

Grey seals, Boreray

The grey seal is the largest species of the UK seal population, with a colony found on Boreray.
Inquisitive in nature, they can often be seen observing tourist boats as they make their way around
the islands.

An't Sail and Geodha na Tarnanach, Boreray
With its steep flanks, castellated towers and cliffs composed of volcanic dolerite and gabbro, it is clear to see why Boreray received its Norse name which roughly translates as 'Fort island'.

Clagan na Rusgachan, An-t Sail Tower, Boreray
At 233m high, Clagan na Rusgachan forms part of the impressive northern profile of Boreray, the
smallest of the Scottish islands to have a summit which reaches over 1,000ft.

The fulmar is a sure prognosticator of the West wind; if it comes to land, no West wind is to be expected for some time, but if it keeps at sea, or goes to sea from the land, whether the wind blow from the South, North or East, or whether it is a perfect and calm, his keeping the sea is always a certain presage of an approaching West wind.

Circling gannets, Boreray
Any visitor to St Kilda will have experienced the sky above filling with gannets who nest on the island in large numbers, with 60,000 recorded in 2013.

The northern gannet

The largest seabird in the gannet family, it can grow to 1m long with a wingspan of nearly 1.8m. They are known for their incredible diving skills, hitting the water in the shape of an arrow, and travelling at speeds of up to 100km/h (62mph), reaching depths of up to 11m.

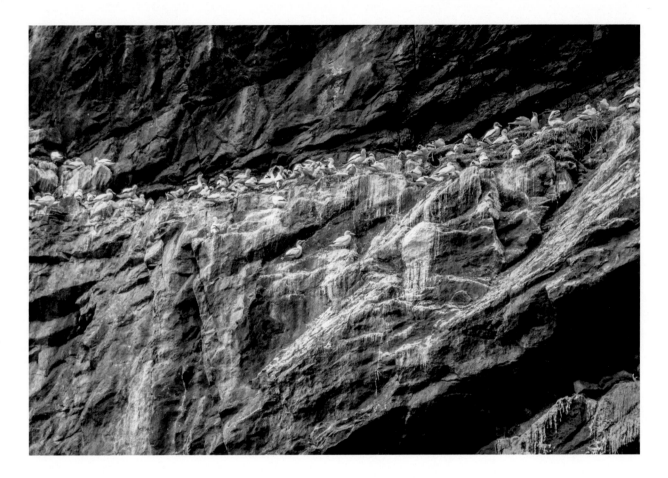

Gannet colony, Boreray

Gannets build their nests on Boreray from seaweed, debris and plants. Due to the birds' habit of leaving their excrement outside of their nests, some nests have grown to around 2m in height. Visitors to Boreray quickly become familiar with the strong smell emanating from the colony.

Clagan na Rusgachab, Boreray

The island of Boreray with its foreboding cliffs, towering stacs and large colony of gannets, has become one of the most recognisable images of the St Kilda archipelago.

Stac Lee (Stac Lì)

Lying to the north-east of Hirta, and only 500m from the cliffs of Boreray, Stac Lee towers above.
A notoriously difficult place to land, it nevertheless has a small two-person bothy, and a colony of
14,000 northern gannets for company.

Stac an Armin (Stac an Àrmainn) and Boreray (Boraraigh)
The 'stack of the warrior' is the highest sea stack in the British Isles, and was once home to the now extinct great auk. The stack has been inhabited for periods of time and contains the ruins of a bothy built by the St Kildans to provide shelter during hunting expeditions.

Leaving St Kilda

The silhouettes of Levenish, Dún, Hirta and Soay can be seen as the boat makes its way back to the mainland. This would have been the last sight of the islands as the St Kildans made their final departure in 1930.

Luath Press Limited

committed to publishing well written books worth reading

LUATH PRESS takes its name from Robert Burns, whose little collie Luath (*Gael.*, swift or nimble) tripped up Jean Armour at a wedding and gave him the chance to speak to the woman who was to be his wife and the abiding love of his life. Burns called one of the 'Twa Dogs' Luath after Cuchullin's hunting dog in Ossian's *Fingal*.
Luath Press was established in 1981 in the heart of Burns country, and is now based a few steps up the road from Burns' first lodgings on Edinburgh's Royal Mile. Luath offers you distinctive writing with a hint of unexpected pleasures.
Most bookshops in the UK, the US, Canada, Australia, New Zealand and parts of Europe, either carry our books in stock or can order them for you. To order direct from us, please send a £sterling cheque, postal order, international money order or your credit card details (number, address of cardholder and expiry date) to us at the address below. Please add post and packing as follows: UK – £1.00 per delivery address; overseas surface mail – £2.50 per delivery address; overseas airmail – £3.50 for the first book to each delivery address, plus £1.00 for each additional book by airmail to the same address. If your order is a gift, we will happily enclose your card or message at no extra charge.

Luath Press Limited

543/2 Castlehill
The Royal Mile
Edinburgh EH1 2ND
Scotland
Telephone: +44 (0)131 225 4326 (24 hours)
email: sales@luath. co.uk
Website: www. luath.co.uk